# SUPER™ QAR

## for Test-Wise Students

### Student Activity Book

This book belongs to:

Wright Group

## The Wishing Sky

Soon they left the woods behind and came out into an open place, high on Big Hill. Madison saw sky all around her.

"Let's sit on that boulder," said Noanie.

Madison climbed onto the huge rock. "This looks like a boat. We can pretend we are sailing through the sky," she said, lying back and looking up. Glittering stars peeked out from the darkness and winked at her.

"Now we must wait for the Wishing Sky," said Noanie.

The wind whistled around Big Hill.

I am the captain of this ship, Madison thought. I will sail through the sky and find a shooting star.

Red lights flashed overhead. "What's that?" asked Madison.

"Just an airplane," said Noanie.

Madison wiggled on the hard rock. "May I have a cookie?"

"You can have one when you see a shooting star," Noanie said.

Madison looked up at the stars and waited. "Noanie, if I make a wish, will it come true?"

"Your wish comes true if that star lands on Earth," Noanie replied.

"How will I know?"

Noanie laughed. "When the wish comes true, of course."

Flash! A star streaked across the sky leaving a silver trail.

"Hurray!" Madison shouted. "I saw one! The Wishing Sky is here!" She closed her eyes and made a wish.

"Hurray! Now you get a star." Noanie gave her a cookie.

As she ate her cookie, Madison gazed at the sky. It was like a sparkling sea. Madison pretended her ship was floating through the night to faraway worlds.

**Directions:** Read each question in column 1. Decide on the answer and write it below. Dicuss the QAR with your partner and write it in column 2.

## QUESTIONS AND ANSWERS

## QAR

1. Do you believe shooting stars make wishes come true? Explain. _____

_____

_____

1. _____

_____

_____

2. What were the red lights that flashed in the night sky? _____

_____

_____

2. _____

_____

_____

3. What does Big Hill look like?

_____

_____

3. _____

_____

_____

4. What do you think Madison was thinking as she ate her cookie? _____

_____

_____

4. _____

_____

_____

_____

5. How will Madison know whether her shooting star lands on Earth?

_____

_____

5. _____

_____

_____

## The Wishing Sky

Whirr! "There's another one!" said Madison, pointing. "Where do shooting stars come from, Noanie?"

"Shooting stars aren't really stars at all. They are meteors—pieces of stone and dust that get in our way as we sail through space," Noanie said.

"They don't look like plain old rocks," said Madison. "They glitter like fireworks."

"That's because they burn up as they fall toward Earth. The sparkles we see are burning stones as they stream through the air."

Madison steered her make-believe ship through rocky places in the sky. Another meteor flashed. "I made a special wish on that one."

"Here's a star you can eat," Noanie said, handing her a cookie. Noanie ate one, too.

"These stars are yummy," said Madison.

Noanie reached into her pocket. "Give me your hand."

Madison held out her hand, and Noanie dropped something cool into her palm. Noanie turned on the flashlight so Madison could see. "This is a meteorite—a shooting star that fell to Earth," she said. "But don't try to eat it!"

In Madison's hand was a small black rock. It felt smooth, but it had holes and marks on it. She turned the stone over and over. "Where did this come from?"

"I found it when I was a little girl," said Noanie. "This kind is called an iron. I would like you to have it to remember our night on Big Hill."

"Thank you, Noanie." Madison put the stone deep in her pocket. "Now I have my own piece of the Wishing Sky."

As Madison and Noanie munched on star cookies, Madison's ship sailed through the starry sea, and the Wishing Sky sparkled all around them.

**Directions:** Think of some questions that could be answered from reading the text on page 4. Write at least two questions in each quadrant. Write the answer to each question in parentheses after the question.

**In the Book—Right There**

**In My Head—On My Own**

**In the Book—Think and Search**

**In My Head—Author and Me**

## Biking to the Max

Racing your BMX bike toward the ten-foot-high half-pipe, you bend over low to gain speed. (A half-pipe is a giant U-shaped structure.) You hit the lip of the pipe and zoom up in the air. You hang there for a moment, and then come down, landing hard on your wheels. This is *nothing* like riding around the block!

BMX freestyle riders perform jumps and stunts in the air. They twist and turn their bikes as they come off a half-pipe. Freestylers also do tricks off a box jump, two ramps connected by a flat board, or a dirt jump, a big mound of earth.

To win a competition, a freestyle rider must receive high scores from judges in these three areas: height of the jump, style, and degree of difficulty.

The stunts and tricks in freestyle biking have funky names such as "candy bar," "nac nac," and "bus driver." These names describe the ways a freestyle rider moves his body and the bike in the air. To learn these moves, riders watch other freestyle riders and practice a lot.

## QUESTION

1. What is a half-pipe?

2. What are some of the stunts a BMX freestyle rider performs?

3. What are freestyle riders judged on during competition?

4. What is the most dangerous part of BMX biking?

5. How is BMX biking different from riding a bike to a friend's house?

1. _____
_____
_____

2. _____
_____
_____

3. _____
_____
_____

4. _____
_____
_____

5. _____
_____
_____

1. _____
_____

2. _____
_____

3. _____
_____

4. _____
_____

5. _____
_____

## Surfing the Sky

With a snowboard fastened to your feet, you hop to the open door of the airplane. The wind whips your face and pulls at your body. The ground far below looks like a bright green carpet. You jump and start surfing the air.

After jumping out of the plane, you are in free fall, going through the air without a parachute, for about seventy seconds. Your body moves at 125 miles per hour.

Sky surfing is performed by a team of two athletes, a sky surfer and a camera flier. The team dives out of a plane flying thirteen thousand feet above the ground.

The sky surfer rides a specially designed surfboard through the air, doing flips, turns, and other stunts. The camera flier stays right alongside his partner, videotaping the jump with a tiny camera fastened to his helmet.

During the first seventy seconds of a jump, sky surfers and their teammates work together to do their trick routines. After that, they need to concentrate on opening their parachutes and landing safely.

**QUESTION AND ANSWER**

**Directions:** Think of several questions that one might ask about the text on page 8. Identify the answer, the QAR, and the strategy needed to answer the question.

| QAR | STRATEGY |
| --- | --- |
| | |

## Arithmetic

Arithmetic is where numbers fly
    like pigeons in and out of your head.
Arithmetic tells you how many you lose or win
    if you know how many you had
    before you lost or won.
Arithmetic is seven eleven all good children
    go to heaven—or five six bundle of sticks.
Arithmetic is numbers you squeeze from your
    head to your hand to your pencil to your paper
    till you get the right answer....
If you have two animal crackers, one good and one bad,
    and you eat one and a striped zebra
    with streaks all over him eats the other,
    how many animal crackers will you have
    if somebody offers you five six seven and you say
    No no no and you say Nay nay nay
    and you say Nix nix nix?
If you ask your mother for one fried egg
    for breakfast and she gives you
    two fried eggs and you eat
    both of them, who is better in arithmetic,
    you or your mother?

by Carl Sandburg

**Directions:** Thinking aloud and using the strategies discussed in class, select the best answer for each question. Below each question, identify the QAR and tell why you think this is the best answer.

1. The poet describes arithmetic using which of the following?

   A. pigeons

   B. fried eggs

   C. animal crackers

   D. all of the above

   QAR: _____

   **Why this is the best answer:**

   _____

   _____

   _____

2. When the poet describes squeezing numbers in arithmetic, what is the order?

   A. paper to pencil to hand to head

   B. hand to head to paper to pencil

   C. head to hand to pencil to paper

   D. head to paper

   QAR: _____

   **Why this is the best answer:**

   _____

   _____

   _____

3. How do you think the poet feels about arithmetic?

   A. it's simple

   B. it's fun

   C. he doesn't have any feelings about it

   D. it's confusing

   QAR: _____

   **Why this is the best answer:**

   _____

   _____

   _____

4. The author wrote this poem to

   A. teach arithmetic

   B. describe pigeons

   C. entertain the reader

   D. solve a math problem

   QAR: _____

   **Why this is the best answer:**

   _____

   _____

   _____

**Directions:** Thinking aloud and using the strategies discussed in class, select the best answer for each question. On the lines below each question, identify the QAR.

1. The admission to the Maritime Museum in Greece is $5 for adults and $3 for children ages 6–12. It costs a total of $37 for 9 people. How many adults and children were in the group?

   A. 7 adults, 2 children
   B. 5 adults, 2 children
   C. 5 adults, 4 children
   D. 4 adults, 5 children

   QAR: _____

2. The white-cheeked gibbon usually lives about 25 years. About every 5 days, it defines its territory with displays of yelling, jumping, and chasing intruders. About how many times will the gibbon make this display during its lifetime?

   A. 125
   B. 1825
   C. 5
   D. 1,000,000

   QAR: _____

3. The dwarf pygmy goby is the smallest fish in the world. There are 1,081 dwarf pygmy gobies at the aquarium. They are divided equally among 23 fish tanks. There is a tank of 15 goldfish nearby. How many dwarf pygmy gobies are in each tank?

   Which information is NOT needed to answer this question?

   A. there are 23 fish tanks
   B. there are 1,081 gobies at the aquarium
   C. there is a tank of 15 goldfish nearby
   D. you need all the information in the problem

   QAR: _____

4. Paul takes 120 pictures of interesting animals. There are 24 pictures on each roll of film. He sends 7 postcards to his friends. Which of the following questions could be answered with the information given?

   A. How many rolls of film does he use?
   B. How many postcards did he buy?
   C. How many different kinds of animals were in his pictures?
   D. How many pictures did not turn out?

   QAR: _____

For questions 5 and 6 use the graph below.

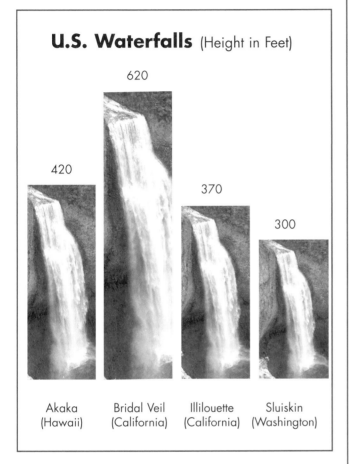

**U.S. Waterfalls** (Height in Feet)

620
420
370
300

Akaka (Hawaii)    Bridal Veil (California)    Illilouette (California)    Sluiskin (Washington)

6. Which of the following questions can NOT be answered from the graph?
   A. How much taller is Bridal Veil Falls than Akaka Falls?
   B. Which waterfall is the shortest?
   C. Which three waterfalls total almost 1,500 feet?
   D. How many meters tall is Bridal Veil Falls?

QAR: _____

5. Which waterfall is the tallest?
   A. Akaka
   B. Bridal Veil
   C. Illilouette
   D. Sluiskin

QAR: _____

**Directions:** Work with a partner to generate several possible answers for each of the following questions.

1. What do raptors hunt? _____

_____

_____

_____

_____


2. How do raptors hunt? _____

_____

_____

_____

_____

_____

_____

_____


3. What is carrion? _____

_____

_____

_____

_____

_____

_____

**Directions:** Brainstorm as many criteria as you can for the following questions. Remember to think about answers for open-ended questions as well as multiple-choice questions. Write your ideas on this page.

1. What makes a good response to a **Think and Search** question?

_____

_____

_____

_____

_____

_____

_____

_____

_____

2. What makes a good response to an **Author and Me** question?

_____

_____

_____

_____

_____

_____

_____

_____

_____

## Falconry

Since ancient times, people have admired raptors for their strength, their intelligence, and their incredible hunting skills. At least three thousand years ago, people realized they could train raptors to help humans hunt for food. As a result, the practice of **falconry** (*FAL kan ree*) was born.

Falconry was first used by people in India and China as a way of hunting for survival. Later, hunting with hawks became the sport of kings. Certain types of raptors were reserved for royalty. The Gyrfalcon was the top of the line.

Today, falconry is practiced only as a sport, not as a means of survival. In recent years, falconry has also become very important in a new way. The grasslands around many airport runways tend to attract flocks of all kinds of birds. These birds can be very dangerous to an airplane. If an airplane hits a bird near the runway, the plane could have trouble taking off or landing. To make sure the runways will be safe, some airports have begun to hire falconers and their raptors to chase away the problem birds.

**Directions:** Read each question and the possible answers. Circle the letter of your answer and identify the QAR. With your group, decide on the evaluation for this answer by using the appropriate rubric, and then write down the score.

1. How did falconry begin?

   **A.** as a sport

   **B.** to keep runways safe

   **C.** to help humans hunt for food

   **D.** as a game for kings

   QAR: _____

   Score: _____

2. Which of the following is true about raptors?

   **A.** they are able to communicate with humans

   **B.** they are in danger of becoming extinct

   **C.** they are an asset to humankind in many ways

   **D.** they have only existed for a few hundred years

   QAR: _____

   Score: _____

3. How do raptors help people now?

   **A.** by hunting for food

   **B.** by eating other birds

   **C.** by keeping runways safe

   **D.** none of the above

   QAR: _____

   Score: _____

4. Why are raptors no longer used to hunt food for people's survival?

   **A.** raptors no longer hunt well

   **B.** people no longer train raptors

   **C.** raptors are at the airport

   **D.** people have better ways of getting food

   QAR: _____

   Score: _____

## Ride the "Vomit Comet"

It's called the "Vomit Comet," and students can't wait to go on it! It's not an amusement park ride, but it can feel like one. The Vomit Comet is a special NASA aircraft used to train astronauts in weightlessness. Two weeks out of the year, NASA also allows college students aboard. The students conduct research on how weightlessness can affect things, and they learn firsthand what zero gravity feels like.

After training on the ground, it's time for the students to fly. Onboard they help bolt their equipment to the floor. Padding covers the floor, walls, and ceiling. All the seats have been removed except for a few rows in the rear. A deep roar of the engines means the first climb has begun. Weightlessness will begin in a few seconds.

The Vomit Comet flies up and down fast like a roller coaster ride. It levels off at 7,315 m (24,000 ft.), and the pilot tells passengers to get ready. First, the plane climbs another 3,048 m (10,000 ft.) at high speed. At the top of the climb, passengers experience weightlessness for about 25 seconds. Then, the plane dives 3,048 m (10,000 ft.) at high speed. Each climb and dive is called a parabola. Every flight has about 32 parabolas, so passengers have about 13 minutes of weightlessness!

At first, weightlessness is scary. That's because you feel like you're falling. Then, you feel excited because you realize you're floating in space!

The dive feels very different. Your body feels much heavier than usual. You can hardly lift your arms. Any movement can make you feel very dizzy. That's because the force you feel pulling down on you is twice the force of gravity.

By the ninth or tenth parabola, some students suffer from motion sickness. They head for the seats in the rear and strap themselves in. It's up to the others to finish the experiments. When it's over, even the sick students say it was the ride of a lifetime. For a short time, they felt just like an astronaut!

**Directions:** With your partner, write four to six questions for the following situation.

Your grandmother cut an article out of the newspaper ("Ride the 'Vomit Comet'") and sent it to you. She does this often, and you know that she'll be calling you in a couple of days to see how you liked the article. She'll also ask you questions about the article (as if she doesn't believe you've read it). You want to be prepared for her call this time, so you decide to write some questions of your own.

**Directions:** Read the text below.

## Voyager to the Bottom of the Ocean

When Cindy Lee Van Dover was growing up, she thought that sea creatures were the most interesting animals. She liked finding weird animals on the beach.

Van Dover never imagined that in 1989 she would become the first female pilot of the submersible *Alvin*. At the bottom of the ocean, she found lots of weird animals.

Van Dover was a submersible pilot until 1991. During this time she took *Alvin* as deep as 3,584 meters. That's more than 2 miles below the surface!

On a typical dive, *Alvin* might take 1 ½ hours to reach the bottom of the ocean. Then the pilot uses the sub's manipulators to gather samples of sea-floor creatures for the scientists. She also takes readings of the water pressures and temperatures outside the submersible. After about five hours on the bottom, the pilot releases weights from the sub, and it floats back to the surface.

During one of Van Dover's trips, *Alvin* got stuck in the mud deep below the ocean. How did this happen? *Alvin* is taken completely apart and then rebuilt every three years. During the rebuilding process some metal flaps were accidentally left off *Alvin's* "belly." The openings allowed mud to fill the bottom.

When Van Dover tried to move the submersible off the ocean bottom, it was stuck. After discussing the problem with engineers on the ship at the surface, Van Dover dropped *Alvin's* weights and waited. Luckily, *Alvin* was now light enough to slowly float back to the surface.

Today Van Dover is an oceanographer who studies the ecology of sea-floor vents. She still dives to the ocean floor about three times a year, but these days she goes as a scientist, not a pilot. Van Dover studies the communities of mussels that live near the vents. When she's not out on a dive gathering samples to study in her laboratory, Professor Van Dover teaches at a university in Virginia.

**Directions:** Answer the following questions after reading the text on page 20. Then write two questions of your own that could be asked about the text. Identify the QAR for each.

1. What is a submersible? _____

_____

_____

QAR: _____

2. What does the pilot of a submersible do? _____

_____

_____

QAR: _____

3. How does *Alvin* get back to the surface? _____

_____

_____

QAR: _____

4. _____

_____

Answer: _____

_____

_____

QAR: _____

5. _____

_____

Answer: _____

_____

_____

QAR: _____

**Directions:** Answer each question and read the texts from *Weird Leela* by Jyotsna Sreenivasan in the order they appear. After each answer, identify the QAR.

1. **How do you think Leela's grandmother will like America?**

   _____

   _____

   **QAR:** _____

2. **How is Leela's grandmother similar to your grandmother?**

   _____

   _____

   **QAR:** _____

As we walk past the bathroom, I see the most popular girl in my class, Crystal, standing against a wall.

"Hi, Crystal!" I shout and wave. "Meet my grandmother!" I grab Ajji's hand and drag her toward Crystal.

Ajji says, "Nice to meet you." Crystal doesn't say anything. She looks at Ajji. Ajji's black-and-gray hair is pulled back into a bun. She has a large, round red dot in the middle of her forehead and a nose stud with a red jewel in it. Ajji is wearing a light blue cloth called a sari that is wrapped and pleated around

her, a pair of Indian sandals called *chappals*, and toe rings on each foot.

My dad calls, "Let's go!" and Ajji walks away. I wave good-bye to Crystal. As I turn to follow Ajji, I hear Crystal mutter, "Weird!" just under her breath.

I feel like I've been slapped. Does Crystal think Ajji is weird? If she thinks Ajji is weird, does she think I'm weird, too?

3. **What happens when Leela introduces her grandmother to Crystal?**

   _____

   _____

   **QAR:** _____

4. **Why do you think Crystal reacted the way that she did?** _____

   _____

   _____

   **QAR:** _____

The next morning, just as I'm heading out the door with my book bag, Ajji comes down the steps into the front hallway.

"Where does your bus pick you up?" Ajji asks.

"Just around the corner."

"In that case, I'll walk with you," Ajji says. She puts on her chappals and throws a shawl around her shoulders.

What if the kids at the bus stop act like Crystal did, when they see Ajji? I'll die of embarrassment.

"No, Ajji. You don't have to."

"It's nothing at all."

"No, really, Ajji. It's okay."

But Ajji is already headed out the door.

5. Why do you think Leela did not want her grandmother to go to the bus stop? _____

_____

_____

_____

QAR: _____

6. What will happen at the bus stop?

_____

_____

_____

QAR: _____

As I get on the bus someone behind me says, "Hey, is that your grandmother?"

I turn to see Nicholas, a boy in my class, pointing out the window at Ajji walking toward the bus. "She arrived yesterday, right?"

I forgot that I told my entire class about Ajji's visit!

"What happened to her forehead?" Nicholas asked. "It looks like it's bleeding."

I don't answer. I just sink lower in my seat.

7. Why does Leela sink lower into her bus seat? _____

_____

_____

QAR: _____

8. Have you ever felt embarrassed by someone else? Explain.

_____

_____

_____

_____

QAR: _____

"What's wrong, Leela?" Anushri asks. "Why didn't you wave to your grandmother?"

"Shh!" I whisper. "Anushri, everyone thinks Ajji is weird!" And I tell her all about Crystal.

"So what?" Anushri says. "You should be happy your grandmother's here. I wish my grandmother could be here to walk me to the bus stop."

When we get to school, Anushri goes to her classroom and I go to mine. No one says anything about Ajji all day —not even Crystal. Right before school ends, my teacher, Ms. Hamilton, asks the class to be quiet. Then she says, "We'll have a special treat this week."

**Questions:** _____

_____

_____

_____

_____

_____

_____

**QAR:** _____

I wonder what the special treat could be. Maybe it's an ice-cream social. We had one of those a few months ago. Or maybe it's a pizza party. I love pizza!

Ms. Hamilton continues, "We all know that Leela's grandmother has come from India for a visit."

What did my grandmother have to do with a special treat?

"And I just learned that Leela's grandmother has agreed to give our class a presentation about life in India on Thursday afternoon!"

**Questions:** _____

_____

_____

_____

_____

_____

_____

_____

**QAR:** _____

On Thursday morning, I go downstairs in my pajamas. Mom and Ajji are both in the kitchen, putting brown *gulab jamun* balls into sugar syrup. Ajji is bringing them to school today for her presentation. They are my favorite Indian dessert, but right now looking at them makes my stomach hurt.

"Mom," I groan. "I think I'm sick."

"Sick?" Mom feels my forehead. "You don't feel warm and you look fine to me. You probably just need some breakfast. Eat your cereal."

On the bus, Anushri says, "You're so lucky that your grandmother's coming to school today!"

"You mean unlucky," I mutter.

Ajji is coming at two o'clock. All morning I feel sick to my stomach. And after lunch, I keep turning around to look at the clock on the back wall of the classroom. As the minutes tick by, the butterflies in my stomach grow worse and worse.

**Questions:** _____

_____

_____

_____

_____

_____

_____

**QAR:** _____

## Other Ways Fossils Form

Imprints, molds, and casts are some types of fossils. Organisms of the past were also preserved in other interesting ways.

Sometimes entire insects became trapped in sticky sap oozing from certain trees. The trapped insects were preserved as the sap hardened into **amber**.

Sometimes entire animals were preserved by being frozen. Mammoths are relatives of modern elephants. Fossilized mammoths have been found in ice and frozen ground in the northern parts of Asia and North America. Bones, hair, skin, flesh, and even internal organs have been preserved.

Many fossils have been discovered in tar pits. Saber-toothed tigers, camels, mammoths, and other animals became stuck in tar pits and died. Their flesh decayed, while their bones sank. The bones were preserved as the tar around them hardened. Rancho La Brea in California is famous for fossils in its tar pits.

Sometimes animal remains are preserved as mummies. They slowly dried out in hot, dry regions like deserts. These fossils have changed little since they formed.

Parts of plants and animals, especially wood and bones, may also be preserved by being **petrified**. Petrified means "turned to stone."

How do you think bones become petrified? Bones have a hard, compact outer layer. Inside is a spongy layer with connected openings, or pores. When a bone is buried, minerals may slowly seep into the pores and fill them. When this happens, the bone is partly petrified. The fossil still has the original bone material. Later the bone itself may be dissolved and replaced by minerals. The bone is then completely petrified.

The woody parts of plants are preserved in the same way as completely petrified bones. Minerals filled the hollow spaces and also replaced all the once-living parts.

**Directions:** Read each question carefully and select the best answer for the first two questions. For questions 3 and 4, write a brief, but complete, response.

1. Which of the following is NOT a way a fossil can form?
   A. by being trapped in tree sap that becomes amber
   B. by laying in minerals
   C. by being petrified
   D. by being frozen in ice

   QAR: _____

   **Why this is the best answer:**

   _____
   _____
   _____

2. How could a whole animal become a fossil?
   A. by being frozen
   B. by falling in a tar pit
   C. by becoming a mummy
   D. all of the above

   QAR: _____

   **Why this is the best answer:**

   _____
   _____
   _____

3. How do you think fossils are discovered?

   _____
   _____
   _____
   _____

   QAR: _____

   **Why this is the best answer:**

   _____
   _____
   _____

4. Which type of fossil interests you the most? Why?

   _____
   _____
   _____
   _____

   QAR: _____

   **Why this is the best answer:**

   _____
   _____
   _____

## What Other Clues Do Fossils Provide?

Fossils also give information about the age of organisms when they died. Annual-growth rings in petrified wood tell the age of fossil trees. Similar footprints of different sizes tell if organisms were young or old.

Fossils also give many clues about the characteristics of organisms. Footprint size is a clue to an animal's size. Distances between footprints may tell whether an animal was walking or running. Footprints also tell if an animal walked on two or four legs.

What types of clues would tell you what animals ate? Meat eaters usually had strong jaws with many pointed teeth. Plant eaters usually had weaker jaws with flat or peglike teeth. Fossilized stomach contents can tell what an animal ate.

Fossils can also tell about past environments. Fossilized aquatic organisms tell where rivers, lakes, and oceans once existed. Fossils also tell that parts of the world were once colder or hotter than they are today. Fossil ferns tell that an area had a warm or hot, moist climate. Fossil evergreen leaves tell that an area was cool.

**Directions:** With a partner, plan carefully what types of questions might appear on a standardized test about the text on page 28. Then write two questions.

## Planning Ideas

_____
_____
_____
_____
_____
_____
_____
_____
_____
_____

## Questions

1. _____
_____
_____
_____

2. _____
_____
_____
_____

## February 12, 1944 continued

Guess what? Yuki used to live in Seattle, too! We made a promise today to be sisters forever. Since neither of us has a real sister, I know we will never break our promise. Ever.

I have one brother, Ben, who is thirteen. He plays first base on our block's baseball team here at Minidoka.

Minidoka is the camp where we have lived for a year and a half. Mama says we must always remember our house back in Seattle. We lived there until the Japanese bombed Pearl Harbor. That day changed our lives forever.

Our family had nothing to do with the bombing, but we had to move to Minidoka just because we are Japanese Americans. Papa says it's not fair. Papa is always right. He told the government men that the United States is also at war with Germany, but our German American neighbors, the Schmidts, were not sent away to a camp.

Mama and Papa are Issei, which means they were born in Japan and then moved to America. The government will not let them become American citizens even though they want to. Ben and I are Nisei, which means our parents were born in Japan and we were born in America. How can we be dangerous? We have never even been to Japan!

We left Seattle on April 28, 1942. We could take only what we could carry. I was seven, and Mama said I could choose one toy. I decided to bring Spotty, my stuffed giraffe.

First a bus took us to Camp Harmony, near Seattle. We stayed at Camp Harmony until August when we moved here to Minidoka. Soldiers put us on the train, and I was scared. I could tell Ben was scared, too. We thought we had done something wrong. The train took us through the mountains and the desert until we arrived at Minidoka.

Papa says that Japanese Americans must prove we are loyal to the United States. He says that we will see justice at the end of the war. I hope so. Papa's never been wrong before.

**Directions:** Complete the chart by answering each question and then identifying the comprehension strategy that helped you answer the question and the QAR.

| QUESTION AND ANSWER | STRATEGY | QAR |
|---|---|---|
| 1. Why did Lily's family have to leave Seattle? | 1. | 1. |
| 2. What is Minidoka? | 2. | 2. |
| 3. How do you think Lily, Yuki, and Ben spend their days at Minidoka? | 3. | 3. |
| 4. How do you think Lily feels about her new home? | 4. | 4. |

## May 17, 1944

Today was a school day. Our school meets in a barrack. When we said the Pledge of Allegiance, I raised my voice when we came to the last words: "with liberty and justice for all."

My best friend Yuki leaned over and giggled. "The guards can hear you all the way over in the watchtowers," she whispered.

I don't care. I think there should be justice for everybody.

Our teacher, Miss Mori, told us we were going to write stories. A few kids groaned, but not me. I love to make up stories. In my stories no one lives in a camp. Everyone lives in a beautiful house with lots of dogs and cats and a big grassy yard. There is no grass here, only acres of sand and sagebrush.

Miss Mori complains that we don't have enough books or pens or paper. Sometimes she gets a package of supplies from white friends outside the camp. That's what happened today. She received a box of beautiful clean paper. We each got one piece.

I had just begun my story when another teacher rushed into our room. She had a worried look on her face.

She told Miss Mori that the wind was starting.

We all knew what that meant. A dust storm! Miss Mori and the other teacher decided to send us home to our barracks. They were afraid the wind would get worse.

They sent us home in pairs. Miss Mori told us to stay together no matter what. I hoped it wouldn't rain. When it rains at Minidoka, the roads turn into slippery, brown mud.

Yuki and I held hands and set out for Block 15. The wind hit us as soon as we stepped out the door. Swirling dust was everywhere. We kept our eyes on the dirt road. Soon dust covered us from head to toe. I could feel dirt in my teeth and hair and eyes.

When Yuki and I got home, we had trouble opening the door. The wind kept knocking it closed. Mama came to our rescue. She helped us inside and hugged us both tight.

Mama walked Yuki home. Now she is worried about Papa and Ben. It's five o'clock, and they are not here yet. Papa is at a meeting. He goes to a lot of meetings.

1. Why don't the Japanese Americans just leave the camp at Minidoka?

_____

_____

2. Why were the children sent home from school on May 17?

_____

_____

3. What were conditions like in the camp? _____

_____

_____

4. What kind of meetings do you suppose Lily's father is attending?

_____

_____

5. How do you feel about this aspect of American history? _____

_____

_____

_____

_____

6. How did the author's style of writing in the form of a journal help you understand this story? _____

_____

_____

_____

# Volcanologist Randy White: U.S. Geological Survey

When a volcano starts to rumble, most people in the area think about leaving. However, some scientists, called volcanologists, head right for the action! It is their job to predict what a volcano is going to do. Randy White is a volcanologist and a member of the Volcano Disaster Assistance Program, a division of the United States Geological Survey (USGS).

White's interest in volcanoes started in high school, when he was a foreign exchange student in Japan. He lived near an erupting volcano called Mount Sakurajima. He was so fascinated by the eruption that he decided to become a volcanologist. After receiving his graduate degree in geophysics from Stanford University in 1974, he went to work for the USGS.

Speed is vital when a volcano is showing signs of waking. White and his team must always be ready to reach a site within 24 hours. When they reach the volcano, they have to answer three important questions. Is the volcano going to erupt? How big an eruption will it be? When will it erupt?

White uses many special instruments in his work. One of the most important is a seismometer. A seismometer measures ground movement and is used to predict earthquake activity. Earthquakes often signal volcanic eruptions. White also takes samples of the atmosphere to check the levels of carbon dioxide and sulfur dioxide. If levels of these gases are high, the volcano might be ready to blow!

In 1991, White and his team were sent to Mount Pinatubo in the Philippines. Using their equipment, they were able to predict the time and size of the eruption. Pinatubo turned out to be the largest volcanic eruption in the world in 80 years. Thanks to the team's predictions, the area was evacuated before the eruption. About 20,000 lives were saved!

**Directions:** Answer the following questions about the text on page 34. Identify the QAR.

1. What is a seismometer? _____

_____

_____

_____

**QAR:** _____

2. How do volcanologists know when volcanoes are ready to erupt?

_____

_____

_____

_____

_____

_____

**QAR:** _____

3. Why are volcanoes potentially dangerous? _____

_____

_____

_____

_____

_____

**QAR:** _____

## Waves of Erosion

Have you ever stood by the ocean and felt a wave pull the sand from under your feet? Waves constantly carry sand away from a beach, bit by bit.

People who live by beaches can watch their "front yards" slowly disappear. Many beach homes are built on stilts. That puts the buildings above water during high tides and storms. However, if the sand supporting the stilts washes away, the houses fall!

If there are cliffs on a shoreline, the pounding waves can wear away the lowest parts. Eventually the cliffs collapse and fall into the water. Then waves slowly break the rocks into smaller pieces. In time the cliffs will become sand.

Stormy winter weather increases erosion. Fierce winds push the waves, giving them the strength to pick up and carry small stones. The stones pound cliffs along with the waves and help break the rocks. The stronger wind also pushes waves farther inland.

Some towns truck in sand to replace what's lost. Other towns build breakwaters close to shore. The stone and concrete breakwaters reduce the force of the waves before they reach shore. An island or a sandbar close to shore serves as a natural breakwater.

Nearly all sand and rock removed by wave erosion is deposited elsewhere. Only a small percentage is carried out to sea.

1. Beach homes may be protected from high tides by
   A. sandbars
   B. stilts
   C. breakwaters
   D. all of the above

   QAR: _____

2. The main idea of this text is that
   A. people should not live near the beach
   B. beaches are affected by erosion
   C. towns should build breakwaters to protect beaches
   D. all of the above

   QAR: _____

3. What is a breakwater?
   A. a type of wave
   B. Stilts that protect houses
   C. a special truck
   D. a barrier that protects the shore

   QAR: _____

4. What happens to sand and rock removed by erosion?
   A. it is deposited elsewhere
   B. it evaporates
   C. it turns into crystals
   D. none of the above

   QAR: _____

5. If you lived in a house by the sea, how would you protect it from wave erosion? _____

   _____

   _____

   _____

   _____

**Directions:** You will be reading a short text titled "All That Glitters Is Not Gold, But It Might Be Neon." Select a topic that you think this article might be about based on its title. In the space below, activate your prior knowledge about this topic by either making a concept web or a list.

## All That Glitters Is Not Gold, But It Might Be Neon

Neon is a colorless, odorless gas. But something magical happens when electrical current passes through neon. The gas and electricity create brightly colored light.

To make neon signs, glassblowers heat glass tubes and bend the softened glass into different shapes or letters. Then, neon gas is pumped into the tubes, and they are sealed shut. Wires conduct electrical current into the tubes through electrodes. Electricity speeds back and forth between electrodes at both ends of the tubes.

The electrons in the neon start to vibrate. As they vibrate, they release excess energy as light.

Neon light glows bright red. Gases similar to neon create different colors. Argon gas, for example, makes bright green light. With different combinations of gases, certain chemicals, and colored glass, neon artists can create more than a hundred colors. Though different materials are used, they're all called "neon signs."

1. What is the first step in making a neon light?
   A. neon gas is pumped into a glass tube
   B. electrodes are attached to a glass tube
   C. the inside of a glass tube is coated with colored powder
   D. a glass tube is heated and bent into a certain shape

   QAR: _____

2. What color light does neon gas make?
   A. red
   B. green
   C. blue
   D. yellow

   QAR: _____

3. What did you learn about neon gas that you did not know before?

   _____

   _____

   _____

   QAR: _____

**Directions:** Fill in the text structures and write definitions for them in the spaces provided. Then identify the most common QAR categories for each text structure.

**Text Structure:** _____

**Definition:** _____

_____

_____

_____

_____

**QAR:** _____


**Text Structure:** _____

**Definition:** _____

_____

_____

_____

_____

_____

**QAR:** _____

**Directions:** Read the following text and answer the questions. Then create a graphic organizer to help you take notes on the article. You will use these notes later to answer questions about lightning.

## How Do You Keep Safe from Lightning?

Lightning gives off energy in several forms—light, heat, and sound. You hear the sound as thunder. Some electrical energy can also travel through an object that has been struck. This energy moves into the ground, or is grounded.

Lightning takes the clearest, shortest path to the ground. Lightning also targets the best conductor.

Lightning can be very dangerous. To be safe, you should follow these simple rules if you hear thunder or see lightning.

1. Stay away from high places, such as hilltops.
2. Stay away from trees and other tall objects.
3. Crouch down if you feel your hair stand on end.
4. Get out of the water.
5. Don't use the telephone.
6. If you are in a car, stay inside. Close the windows and doors.
7. Don't touch electrical devices or anything made of metals.

What text structure has the author used to organize this text?

_____

What do you know about this text structure? _____

_____

What QAR might you anticipate for this text structure? _____

_____

**Directions:** Read the following text from *What a Plant!* by Christine Latham and answer the questions below. Then create a graphic organizer to help you take notes from the article. You will use these notes later to answer questions about jumping beans.

## Jumping Beans

The *Mexican jumping bean* is really the seed of the arrow plant from Mexico. The secret of its movement is a tiny caterpillar.

This caterpillar is the larva of a moth called *Cydia saltitans*, which lays its eggs on the arrow plant flowers. When a caterpillar hatches out of an egg, it burrows into a growing seed. Soon it is surrounded by a hard outer shell, or seed case.

The seed case hardens and drops onto the hot desert floor. When the caterpillar inside the seed case gets too hot, it flips its body. With each flip, the seed jumps. These caterpillars can jump around like this for several months. Eventually the caterpillar cuts a lid in the seed wall. When the caterpillar becomes an adult moth, the moth pushes its way outside the seed.

What text structure has the author used to organize this text?

_____

What do you know about this text structure? _____

_____

What QAR might you anticipate for this text structure? _____

_____

**Directions:** Answer the following questions from the two articles "How Do You Keep Safe from Lightning?" and "Jumping Beans." Use the graphic organizers on pages 41 and 42 to help you. Next to each question, identify the QAR.

1. Which of the following is it okay to do if you hear thunder or see lightning?
   A. stay in the swimming pool
   B. use an umbrella
   C. go on top of your house to see the storm
   D. find a low spot and crouch down

2. When electrical energy moves into the ground, it is
   A. thunder
   B. grounded
   C. lightning
   D. none of the above

3. Which of these things happens first?
   A. the seed drops to the desert floor
   B. the caterpillar cuts a lid in the seed wall
   C. a newly hatched caterpillar burrows into a growing seed
   D. the caterpillar flips its body over

4. What causes a Mexican jumping bean to jump?
   A. it doesn't jump, that's just a myth
   B. the heat from the desert causes the seed to expand
   C. there is a moth inside the seed
   D. none of the above

5. Explain what happens to the energy given off by lightning.

_____

_____

_____

_____

6. Why do you think people call this plant a *jumping bean*?

_____

_____

_____

_____

**Directions:** Fill in the text-structure chart below.

| TEXT STRUCTURE | FEATURES | QAR CATEGORIES |
|---|---|---|
| Simple List | | |
| Sequence | | |
| Description | | |
| Explanation | | |

## Did Glaciers Exist in the Past?

Scientists have learned about glaciers of the past by studying present-day glaciers and their features. Some of these features are scratched bedrock and U-shaped valleys. Other glacial features include erratics and outwash plains. Erratics (*i RAT iks*) are isolated boulders left behind by a glacier. Outwash plains are gravel, sand, and clay carried from glaciers by melting water and streams. They are deposited over large areas.

Glacial features are found today far from where glaciers now exist. They are evidence that glaciers once covered much larger parts of the world than they do today. Periods of very cold temperatures and many glaciers are called ice ages. During the ice ages, vast ice sheets as thick as several kilometers covered as much as one-third of Earth's surface. Temperatures were very low. Snowfall was heavy. Only places far from the glaciers were even slightly warm. As more and more water became ice, the oceans were greatly reduced in size.

Periods of warmer weather existed between ice ages. They are known as interglacial periods. Some scientists think that we are now in an interglacial period. They also believe that far in the future, Earth will undergo another ice age.

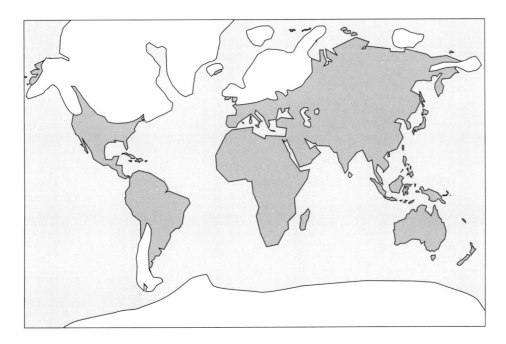

**Glacial areas**

**Directions:** Answer the questions below about the text on page 45. Then create a graphic organizer to help you take notes on the article.

1.  What text structure has the author used to organize this text?

    _____

2.  What do you know about this text structure?

    _____

    _____

    _____

3.  What QAR categories might you anticipate for this text structure?

    _____

    _____

    _____

**Directions:** Answer the following questions about the article "Did Glaciers Exist in the Past?" You may need to refer to the article or your graphic organizer. Note the QAR after each question.

1. Which of these happened during the ice ages?

    **A.** temperatures were very low     **C.** sheets of ice covered Earth's surface

    **B.** snowfall was heavy     **D.** all of the above

    **QAR:** _____

2. What features today help scientists study glaciers of long ago?

    **A.** erratics     **C.** oceans

    **B.** rivers     **D.** interglacial periods

    **QAR:** _____

3. In which of the following ways can glaciers change the land?

    **A.** gravel, sand, and clay can be carried away

    **B.** boulders can be left on the land

    **C.** U-shaped valleys can be formed

    **D.** all of the above

    **QAR:** _____

4. Do you believe we are in an interglacial period? Why or why not?

    _____

    _____

    **QAR:** _____

5. The people of Iceville are worried about a nearby glacier. They are thinking of building a large fence to keep it in place. Do you think their idea will work? Explain. _____

    _____

    _____

    _____

    **QAR:** _____

## Smoky City

Rachel and her family lived in one of the few areas left in southwestern Pennsylvania that had not been tarnished by the smoke and soot from coal-burning factories and steel mills. Pittsburgh, a city close to Rachel's home, was called the "Smoky City" because of its polluted air.

Before Rachel was born, her father, Robert Warden Carson, purchased sixty-five acres of countryside along the Allegheny River. He had hoped to sell it in parcels to people from Pittsburgh. But Mr. Carson's dream was not to be. The year Rachel was born, 1907, an economic depression hit the nation leaving people with no money to invest in land. A coal mining company offered to pay cash to tunnel under his property. But Rachel's father refused to sell his land to an industry that polluted the environment.

Instead, the Carson family made a living by farming a small apple orchard on the property. Rachel's father purchased a cow, pigs, and chickens to provide for the family's needs. Together with her older sister Marian and brother Robert, Rachel picked apples, milked the cow, and gathered eggs. Learning to care for the trees and animals that gave them food taught Rachel, at an early age, about the important bond between humans and other living things.

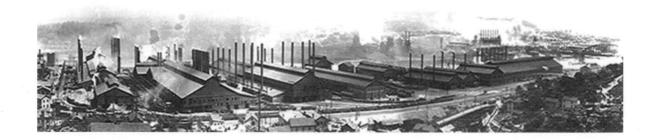

**Directions:** Circle the best answer for questions 1 and 2 and write a complete response for questions 3 and 4.

1. Which of the following do we know about Rachel Carson as a young girl?
   A. she was born during an economic depression
   B. she loved taking care of trees and animals
   C. she lived alongside the Allegheny River
   D. all of the above

2. Why did Rachel's father refuse to sell his land?
   A. he did not need the money
   B. the company that wanted to buy it polluted the air
   C. he needed the river for fishing and transporting food
   D. none of the above

3. What impact do you think Rachel's childhood will have on her as an adult?

   _____

   _____

   _____

   _____

   _____

   _____

4. Why is this text called "Smoky City"? _____

   _____

   _____

   _____

   _____

   _____

   _____

## The Web of Life

Rachel looked forward to the half-mile walk to school along the river. Watching birds dive for food and beavers build their homes was as fascinating to her as learning a new subject in school.

Sometimes the walk was physically too much for her. Rachel had had scarlet fever as a young girl, and her health was fragile. When illness kept her home, her mother helped her keep up with schoolwork.

Missing school did not help the shy, quiet Rachel make friends. Her older sister and brother were already grown, and she was the only child at home. But Rachel did not mind being alone.

Rachel attended a different school for her last two years of high school. Her classmates respected her as an excellent student, though few of them knew her well.

After she graduated from high school in 1925, Rachel received a scholarship to Pennsylvania College for Women in Pittsburgh (now called Chatham College). Rachel's mother had never gone to college. She was thrilled that her daughter now had the chance. The scholarship would pay for some of Rachel's schooling. But where would they get the rest of the money? Mrs. Carson decided to sell the family silver and china. Seeing her daughter follow her dream of becoming a writer was worth the sacrifice.

Once in college, Rachel began to develop new interests. She became a reporter for the student newspaper and wrote stories for the college literary journal.

During her sophomore year, she signed up for a required class in biology. Little did Rachel know that it would change her life. At first, Rachel did not look forward to a class that involved dissecting frogs. But this biology class was different. The professor, Mary Scott Skinker, had a passion for science. She taught her students about the relationship between all living things, now known as ecology. This "web of life" linked plants, animals, and humans together with each one dependent upon the others for survival.

**Directions:** Circle the best answer for questions 1 through 3. Write complete responses for questions 4 and 5.

1. Why didn't Rachel go to school regularly?

    **A.** her mother wanted to teach her at home

    **B.** the walk was too long

    **C.** she had scarlet fever as a child and was often sick

    **D.** there was no school close to their home

2. What did Rachel do in college?

    **A.** became a reporter for the school newspaper

    **B.** took a biology class

    **C.** learned about the "web of life"

    **D.** all of the above

3. What kind of childhood do you think Rachel had?

    **A.** sad              **C.** boring

    **B.** lonely         **D.** crazy

4. Why do you think Rachel liked biology so much? _____

    _____

    _____

    _____

    _____

5. What do you think it was like for Rachel to go to college?

    _____

    _____

    _____

    _____

    _____

**Directions:** Answer each question thoroughly.

1. What is QAR? _____

_____

_____

_____

_____

2. How do you use QAR? _____

_____

_____

_____

_____

_____

_____

_____

3. When do you use QAR? _____

_____

_____

_____

_____

_____

_____

_____

**Directions:** Think about the knowledge you have gained about QAR this year. How have you changed the way you think about answering questions?

**Directions:** Brainstorm a list of the various settings and situations where you can use QAR during the rest of the school year.

**Directions:** Organize the information on page 54 so that it is more useful. You may use any kind of graphic organizer you would like or an outline. Include enough detail and labels to ensure your organization will be clear to others.

QAR

Reflections
Journal